The
Great Plague

An eyewitness account

Tim Vicary

Oxford University Press 1993

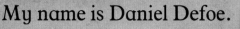

My name is Daniel Defoe.
I am a writer. My most famous book is *Robinson Crusoe*.
When I was five, in 1665, there was a terrible plague in
London. Many people died.

I asked my uncle, Henry Foe, to tell me about it.
This is the story he told. I wrote it down for him.

Henry Foe's story

In December 1664 a ship came from Holland.
A week later, two people died from the plague.
Then ten died, then thirty. People tried to hide it.
'It's not the plague, it's spotted fever,' they said.

But in January five hundred people died in one week.
Most of the rich people left London.
The King and his friends went to Oxford.

Most of the poor people stayed on in London, and so did the Lord Mayor.
I walked around the city to see what was happening.

People tried to sell me charms and medicines.

'Wear this, drink this,' they said. 'Then you'll be safe.'

Other people were so frightened that they paid money for these cures.

But it was all rubbish. Most of them still died.

People knew they were ill when they got red, hard painful
lumps.
They got headaches, they sweated and couldn't keep still.
The doctors tried to make the lumps burst, or cut
them open.
It hurt terribly, but it didn't help much.

After a day or two most people with lumps were dead.
Nearly everyone in our street died.

If anyone had the plague, a searcher locked them in their
house, and painted a red cross on the door.
A watchman stood outside with a stick.

Often healthy people were locked in too.
The healthy people didn't like this,
so they tried to trick the watchmen.
They climbed out of the windows and ran away.

At night, carts came by to take the dead bodies away.
'Bring out your dead!' the carters cried.

Once, I saw a man fall asleep on a wall.
The carters put him in their cart with the bodies.
'Help! Let me out!' he shouted. The carters ran away.
'It's a ghost!' they cried.

We all tried to stay away from sick people.
'We can catch the plague from their smell,' we thought.
'Or from their breath, when they sneeze.'
We held flowers and perfumes in front of our noses.

Children sang this song:
Ring a ring of roses,
A pocket full of posies,
Atishoo, atishoo,
We all fall down!
Can you understand what these words mean?

In shops we put money in buckets of vinegar to keep it clean.

16

Once, a man left a purse in a shop.
The shopkeeper was afraid to touch the money,
so he poured gunpowder on the purse and lit it with
a candle.
Then he dropped the money into a bucket with a pair
of tongs.

'My family is sick,' a boatman told me.
'I can't go near them.'
'But that's terrible!' I said. 'You *must* help your family!'
'Oh, I do, sir,' he said. 'Watch this.'

18

He put some food on a stone, stood back, and shouted. Slowly, his sick wife came out for the food. The man watched, crying.

'You poor, poor people,' I said.

By September, fewer people were dying.
We felt happier, and began to talk to each other again.
'Thank God,' we said. 'The Great Plague is over!'

What had caused the plague? Some doctors said:
'The plague is in sick people's breath.
If they blow on a glass, we see tiny dragons and worms
on it.'
It was a good idea, but it wasn't quite right.

In 1665, people didn't understand what caused the plague.
In fact, the plague came from rats.
The rats had germs in their blood, and fleas bit the rats.
Then the fleas bit people, and the germs went into their blood.

There aren't many rats or fleas in houses today.
So we don't have plagues like that any more.

There are rats hiding on nearly every page of this book.
How many can you find?

Oxford University Press, Walton Street, Oxford OX2 6DP

Oxford   New York   Toronto
Delhi   Bombay   Calcutta   Madras   Karachi
Kuala Lumpur   Singapore   Hong Kong   Tokyo
Nairobi   Dar es Salaam   Cape Town
Melbourne   Auckland   Madrid

and associated companies in
Berlin   Ibadan

Oxford is a trade mark of Oxford University Press
© Tim Vicary 1993

Illustrations by Nick Harris

0 19 917232 3
0 19 917242 0 (pack of 6)

Typeset by Pentacor PLC, High Wycombe, Bucks
Printed in Hong Kong